Thank-You For Atten...
Chestermere Pride 2018!
— The WCS Team
www.strathmoreshelter.com
(FB) → @wheatlandcrisissociety

Through It All

Domestic Violence Survivor's Edition

A Gratitude & Coloring Journal

Written by J. Jackson
Foreword by Laura T. Johnson

ISBN:978-0-9836270-6-7
Cover Design By: J. Jackson
Interior Design By: J.Jackson

Dear Survivors,

We all have a fountain of strength that keeps us going for our family, our friends, and most importantly ourselves. Every day we find a reason to carry on. You must realize that you don't have to lie in the bed you made. You can always get up!

Don't believe that there isn't anything better out there for you. If you are in an abusive relationship, be it physical or verbal; please do not believe that this is the way things should be or that things will eventually get better. Because they won't. There is life after abuse.

Never be ashamed of what you went through. It only makes you stronger. Just remember that God didn't bring you this far for you to give up. You have the strength to change your situation. To change your life. I know at times it feels hopeless, but never give up. Go to your family, friends, even the police. You don't have to go through this alone. I went through two years of abuse without telling anyone. Afraid of what my family might do or even say. I kept things bottled up and it took a toll on me both mentally and physically.

But I'm grateful for so many things. The number one thing I'm grateful for is God not listening when I prayed for death. He believed in me and knew that I would make a difference. So, I beg of you to find the strength to fight your way back to a life worth living. You're worth that fight. Even when you feel like giving up, remember that through it all God will carry you.

Remember that you can overcome anything; you can come out of anything. Be strong, pray often, because prayer truly does changes things.

Love & Strength,
Laura T. Johnson
Author of Where Would I Be

http://authorlauratjohnson.org

4

Introduction

If you watch the news you've probably noticed that there is a major increase in cases of domestic violence. On average, 24 people per minute become victims of domestic violence; that includes men. Domestic violence affects over 12 million people a year. I'm going to let that sink in. And while you think on that, try this: 1 in 4 women and 1 in 7 men have suffered at the hands of their partner. Why are these numbers so important? Because each one stands for a life. Each number represents a life that has been affected by this senseless act. Be it physical, verbal, mental, or financial, abuse is WRONG! If you or someone you know is suffering from IPV (Intimate Partner Violence), please contact The National Domestic Violence Hotline at: 1-800-799-7233/1-800-787-3224 (TTY) Website: www.thehotline.org.

In a world where much in life is expected and taken for granted, there are still the simple things that bring peace of mind. A simple "Thank You", for instance could certainly be one of those things. In my gratitude I have found a little slice of heaven in my journal. I enjoy taking time each day to record all that I am grateful for. It forces me to take a look at all that I have and say a simple thank you. It's such a simple practice with such a huge reward. I hope you find the practice as rewarding as I do as you go through the different sections of this journal.

How to use this book

Read and reflect on the written passages of each section of the book. Let the words play around in your mind before writing your answers to the questions asked in each section.

Benefits of Journaling and Coloring Therapy

Let's face it, our lives can be stressful and we often need a way to calm our minds. Coloring has always been thought of as a fond childhood pastime, but not anymore. Coloring and art therapy has been pushing itself to the forefront for several years now. It's great for helping to develop patience, focus and attention to detail. So grab your colored pencils, crayons and/or colored markers and let the stress melt away as you color in the beautiful mandalas within these pages. Focus your mind on your personal affirmation while you destress.

Let's Get Started!

SELF-LOVE

I think the most important thing in life is self-love, because if you don't have self-love, and respect for everything about your own body, your own soul, your own capsule, then how can you have an authentic relationship with anyone else?

Shailene Woodley

Do you love yourself? Describe in detail how you love yourself.

Five Things I'm Grateful For:

-
-
-
-
-

COURAGE

We gain strength, and courage, and confidence by each experience in which we really stop to look fear in the face... we must do that which we think we cannot.

Eleanor Roosevelt

Describe a time when you stood courageous against something you feared. How did you feel once your personal strength kicked in?

Five Things I'm Grateful For:

-
-
-
-
-

HEALING

Did I offer peace today? Did I bring a smile to someone's face? Did I say words of healing? Did I let go of my anger and resentment? Did I forgive? Did I love? These are the real questions. I must trust that the little bit of love that I sow now will bear many fruits, here in this world and the life to come.

Henri Nouwen

You've been through a horrible ordeal that no one should have to endure. Have you healed from that ordeal? If you have, describe below how you went about doing that? If you haven't yet, describe below how you plan to start the healing process.

Five Things I'm Grateful For:

-
-
-
-
-

SURVIVAL

We don't even know how strong we are until we are forced to bring that hidden strength forward. In times of tragedy, of war, of necessity, people do amazing things. The human capacity for survival and renewal is awesome.

Isabel Allende

Congratulations. You survived. Describe below how you will continue to survive as you heal and learn to love yourself. Will you pray daily? Will you take a self-defense class? Have lunch with friends? Confide in a friend? Keep a journal? Share your story? How will you continue to survive?

Five Things I'm Grateful For:

-
-
-
-
-

HAPPINESS

I, not events, have the power to make me happy or unhappy today. I can choose which it shall be. Yesterday is dead, tomorrow hasn't arrived yet. I have just one day, today, and I'm going to be happy in it.

Groucho Marx

Happiness is an inside job and you are uniquely qualified. Describe below what your ultimate happy is and how you plan to achieve it.

Five Things I'm Grateful For:

-
-
-
-
-

FREEDOM

Freedom means you are unobstructed in living your life as you choose. Anything less is a form of slavery.

Wayne Dyer

You're free! You are now in control of what happens to you next. Describe below what your freedom means to you. What new opportunities are you ready to take advantage of to assert your new independence?

Five Things I'm Grateful For:

- _____
- _____
- _____
- _____
- _____

BLAME

When a man has been consistently battering his wife, he shouldn't expect a bouquet of roses from her the morning after he promises to stop.

Joe Slovo

What happened to you was NOT your fault! What happened to you was NOT your fault! What happened to you was NOT your fault! Below create a personal mantra to meditate on daily. Tweek it as often as you need to stay uplifted in the fact you did nothing wrong.

Five Things I'm Grateful For:

-
-
-
-
-

GROWTH

The fact is, that to do anything in the world worth doing, we must not stand back shivering and thinking of the cold and danger, but jump in and scramble through as well as we can.

Robert Cushing

You've come a long way, even if today is day 1 the hardest step has been taken. Describe below how you've grown since your ordeal.

Five Things I'm Grateful For:

-
-
-
-
-

WISDOM

Some of the best lessons we ever learn we learn from our mistakes and failures. The error of the past is the wisdom of the future.

Tryon Edwards

Describe below the wisdom you've accumulated during and after your ordeal. What lessons have you learned in freeing yourself from chaos?

Five Things I'm Grateful For:

-
-
-
-
-

Notes:

If you watch the news you've probably noticed that there is a major increase in cases of domestic violence. On average, 24 people per minute become victims of domestic violence; that includes men. Domestic violence affects over 12 million people a year. I'm going to let that sink in. And while you think on that, try this: 1 in 4 women and 1 in 7 men have suffered at the hands of their partner. Why are these numbers so important? Because each one stands for a life. Each number represents a life that has been affected by this senseless act. Be it physical, verbal, mental, or financial, abuse is WRONG! If you or someone you know is suffering from IPV (Intimate Partner Violence), please contact The National Domestic Violence Hotline at: 1-800-799-7233/1-800-787-3224 (TTY) Website: www.thehotline.org.

If you watch the news you've probably noticed that there is a major increase in cases of domestic violence. On average, 24 people per minute become victims of domestic violence; that includes men. Domestic violence affects over 12 million people a year. I'm going to let that sink in. And while you think on that, try this: 1 in 4 women and 1 in 7 men have suffered at the hands of their partner. Why are these numbers so important? Because each one stands for a life. Each number represents a life that has been affected by this senseless act. Be it physical, verbal, mental, or financial, abuse is WRONG! If you or someone you know is suffering from IPV (Intimate Partner Violence), please contact The National Domestic Violence Hotline at: 1-800-799-7233/1-800-787-3224 (TTY) Website: www.thehotline.org.

Made in the USA
Middletown, DE
06 March 2018